Boyzone

Wise Publications
London/New York/Paris/Sydney/
Copenhagen/Madrid/Tokyo

Exclusive Distributors:
Music Sales Limited
8/9 Frith Street, London W1V 5TZ, England.
Music Sales Pty Limited
120 Rothschild Avenue, Rosebery, NSW 2018, Australia.

Order No. AM966526
ISBN 0-7119-8401-8
This book © Copyright 2000 by Wise Publications

Compiled by Nick Crispin
Music arranged by Stephen Duro
Music processed by Allegro Reproductions
Cover photograph (Ronan Keating) courtesy of London Features International

Printed in the United Kingdom by
Halstan & Co Limited, Amersham, Buckinghamshire.

Your Guarantee of Quality
As publishers, we strive to produce every book to the highest commercial standards.
The music has been freshly engraved and the book has been carefully designed to minimise
awkward page turns and to make playing from it a real pleasure.
Particular care has been given to specifying acid-free, neutral-sized paper made from pulps
which have not been elemental chlorine bleached. This pulp is from farmed sustainable forests
and was produced with special regard for the environment.
Throughout, the printing and binding have been planned to ensure a sturdy, attractive publication
which should give years of enjoyment.
If your copy fails to meet our high standards, please inform us and we will gladly replace it.

Music Sales' complete catalogue describes thousands of titles and is available in full colour sections
by subject, direct from Music Sales Limited. Please state your areas of interest
and send a cheque/postal order for £1.50 for postage to:
Music Sales Limited, Newmarket Road, Bury St. Edmunds, Suffolk IP33 3YB.

www.musicsales.com

A Different Beat

**Words & Music by Martin Brannigan, Stephen Gately, Ronan Keating,
Shane Lynch, Ray Hedges & Keith Duffy**

Moderately

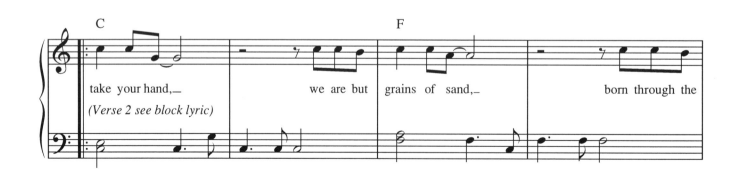

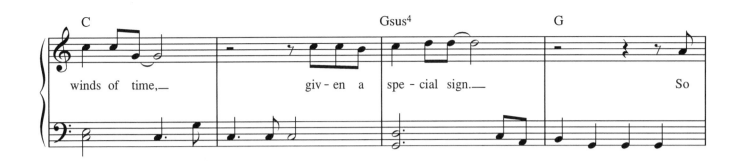

winds of time,— giv-en a spe-cial sign.— So

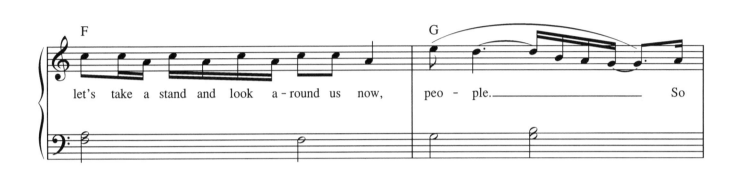

let's take a stand and look a-round us now, peo - ple.———————— So

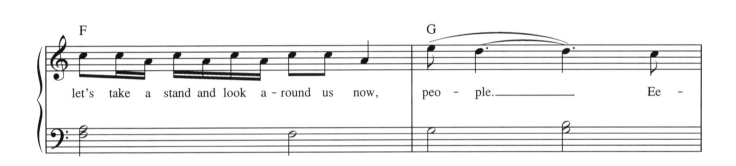

let's take a stand and look a-round us now, peo - ple.————— Ee -

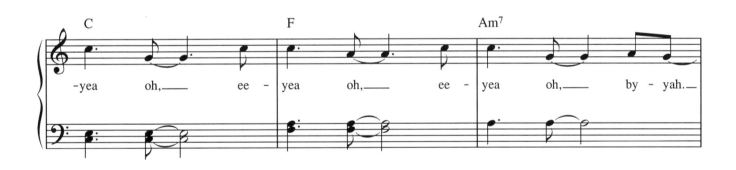

-yea oh,—— ee - yea oh,—— ee - yea oh,—— by - yah.—

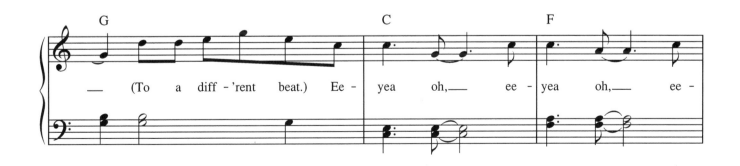

— (To a diff-'rent beat.) Ee - yea oh,—— ee - yea oh,—— ee -

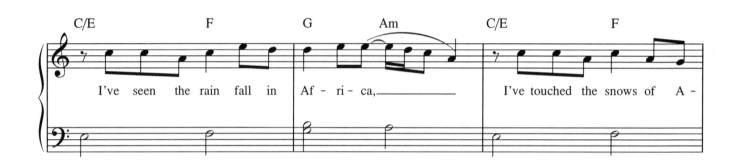

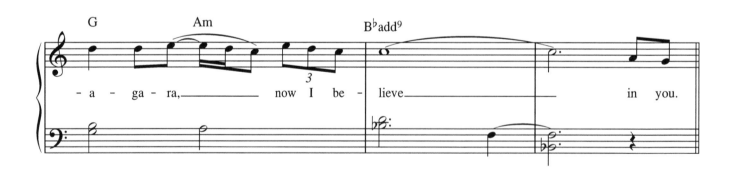

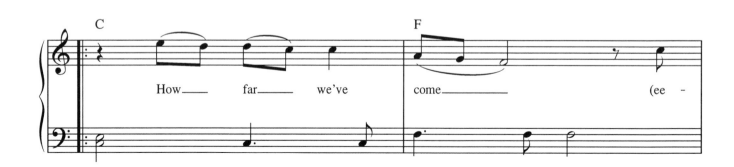

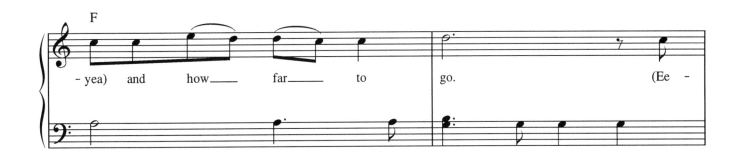

- yea) and how___ far___ to go. (Ee -

- yea.) How___ far___ we've come___ (ee -

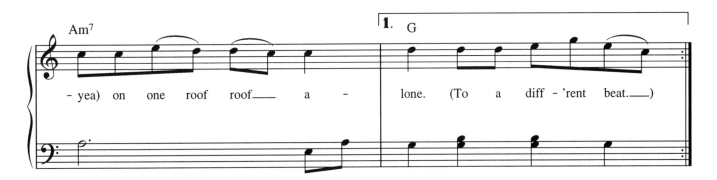

- yea) on one roof roof___ a - lone. (To a diff - 'rent beat.___)

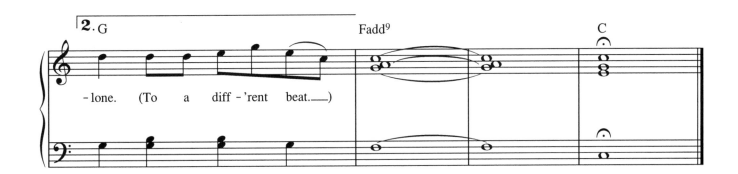

-lone. (To a diff - 'rent beat.___)

Verse 2:

Humanity has lost face,
Let's understand its grace,
Each day, one at a time,
Each life, including mine.

Let's take a stand and look around us now,
People,
So let's take a stand and look around us now'
People, oh people, oh people.

All That I Need

Words & Music by Evan Rogers & Carl Sturken

Moderately

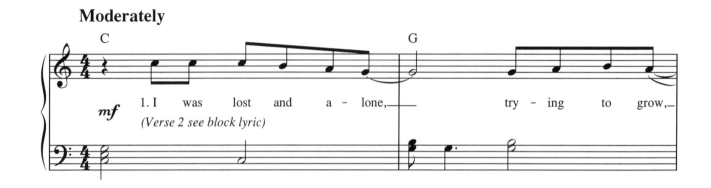

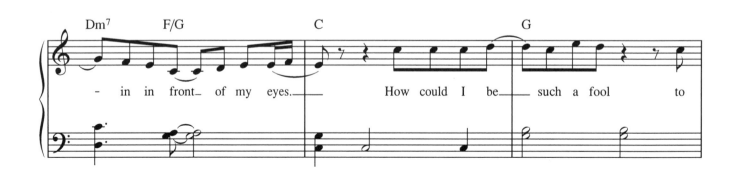

let go of love__ and break all__ of the rules? Girl, when you walked

__ out that door, left a hole__ in my heart and now I__ know for sure;__

__ You're the air that I breathe__ girl, you're all that I need.

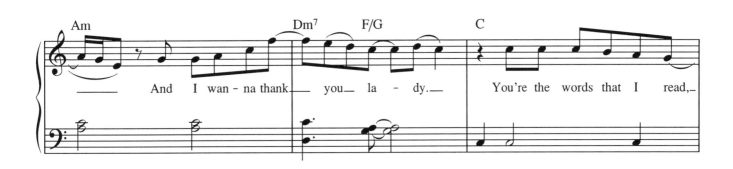

__ And I wan-na thank__ you__ la-dy.__ You're the words that I read,__

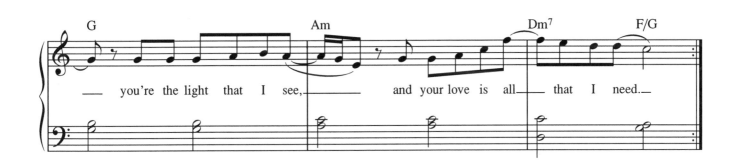

__ you're the light that I see,__ and your love is all__ that I need.__

9

Verse 2:

I was searching in vain, playing your game
Had no-one else but myself left to blame
You came into my world, no diamonds or pearls
Could ever replace what you gave to me girl
Just like a castle of sand
Girl I almost let love
Slip right out of my hand
And just like the flower needs rain
I will stand by your side
Through the joy and the pain.

You're the air that I breathe *etc.*

Baby Can I Hold You

Words & Music by Tracy Chapman

Moderately

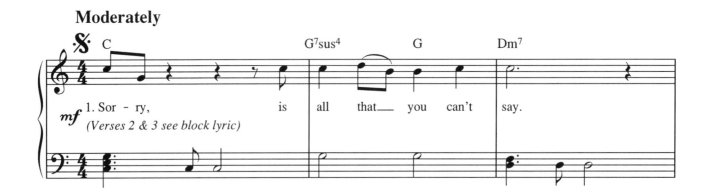

1. Sor - ry, is all that you can't say.
(Verses 2 & 3 see block lyric)

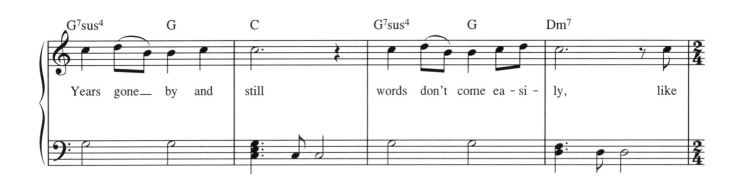

Years gone by and still words don't come ea-si-ly, like

sor ry, like sor-ry. 2. For- -give me.

But you can say ba - by, ba-by can I hold you to-

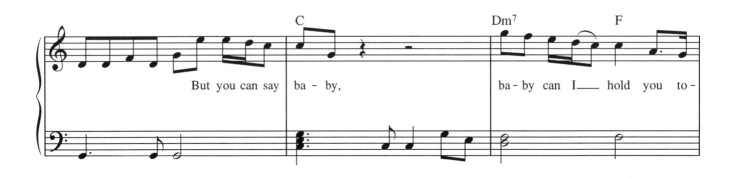

(Ba - by if I told you.—)   (Ba - by,—)You'd be mine.

(Ba - by if I told you.—)   (Ba - by,—)You'd be mine.

(Ba - by if I told you.)   Ba - by can I hold___ you?

Verse 2:

Forgive me is all that you can't say
Years gone by and still
Words don't come easily
Like forgive me, forgive me.

Verse 3:

I love you is all that you can't say
Years gone by and still
Words don't come easily
Like I love you, I love you.

Every Day I Love You

Words & Music by Frank J. Myers, Gary Baker & Jerry Williams

Moderately

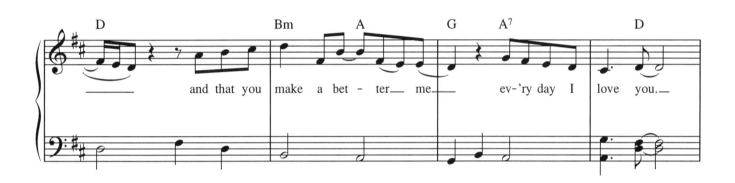

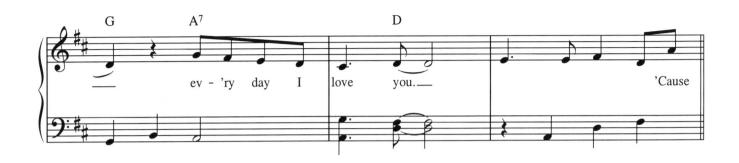

ev - 'ry day I love you.___ 'Cause

I be - lieve___ that des - ti - ny___ is out___ of our___ con -

- trol. (Don't you know that?) And you'll nev - er live___ un - til___ you___ love___ with

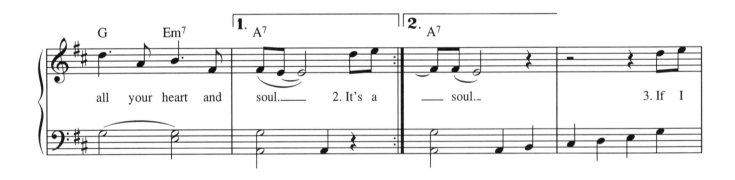

all your heart and soul.___ 2. It's a ___ soul.__ 3. If I

asked would you_ say yes?___ To - geth-er we're the ve - ry best,___ I know that

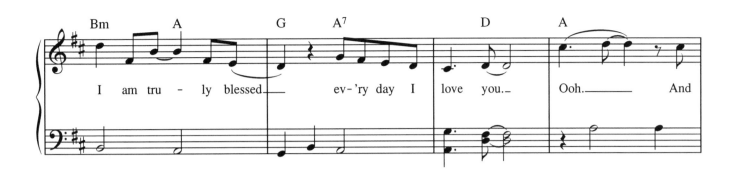

I am tru – ly blessed___ ev-'ry day I love you.___ Ooh._____ And

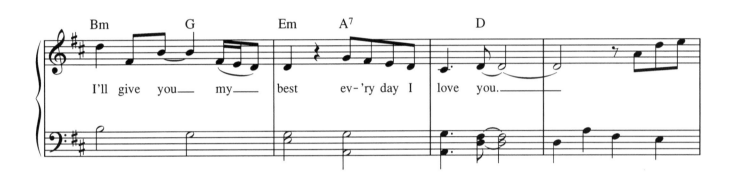

I'll give you___ my___ best ev-'ry day I love you.___

Oh yeah.__

Verse 2:
It's a touch when I feel bad
It's a smile when I get mad
All the little things I have
Everyday I love you.
Instrumental break.

'Cause I believe *etc.*

Father And Son

Words & Music by Cat Stevens

Moderately

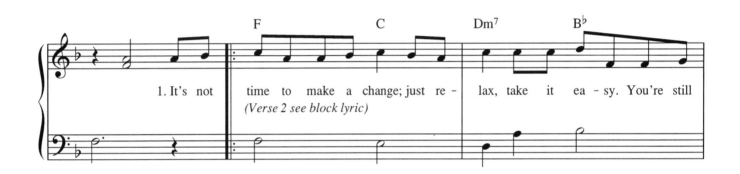

1. It's not time to make a change; just re-lax, take it ea - sy. You're still
(Verse 2 see block lyric)

young, that's your fault; there's so much you have to know.— Find a girl,—

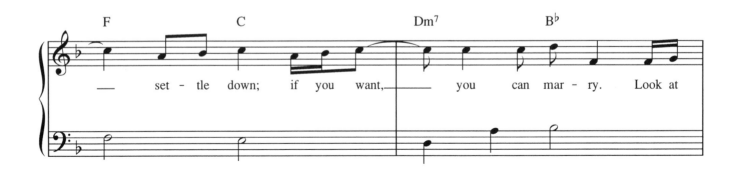

— set - tle down; if you want,——— you can mar - ry. Look at

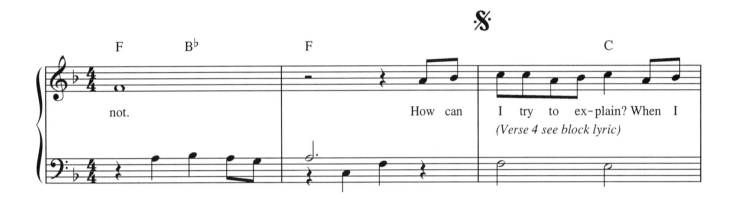

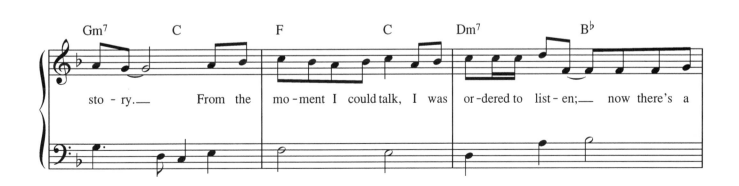

19

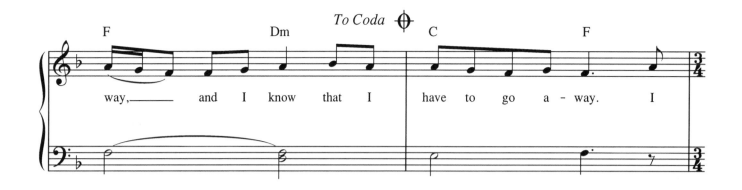

way,———— and I know that I have to go a-way. I

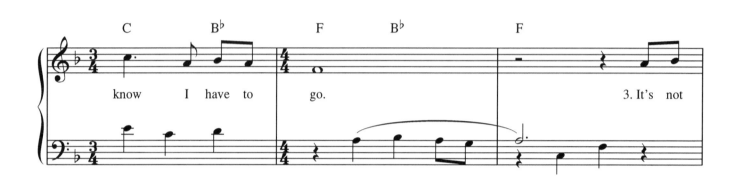

know I have to go. 3. It's not

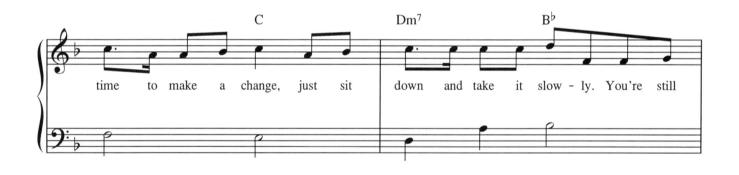

time to make a change, just sit down and take it slow-ly. You're still

young, that's your fault; there's so much you have to go through. Find a

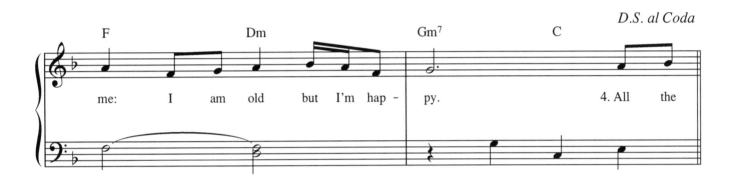

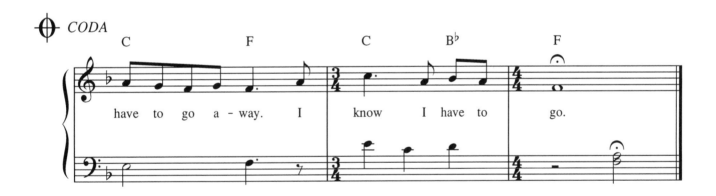

Verse 2:

I was once like you are now;
And I know that it's not easy
To be calm when you've found something going on.
But take your time, think a lot;
Think of everything you've got.
For you will still be here tomorrow,
But your dreams may not.

Verse 4:

All the times that I've cried,
Keeping all the things I knew inside;
And it's hard, but it's harder to ignore it.
If they were right I'd agree,
But it's them they know, not me;
Now there's a way, and I know
That I have to go away.
I know I have to go.

I Love The Way You Love Me

Words & Music by Chuck Cannon & Victoria Shaw

Moderately

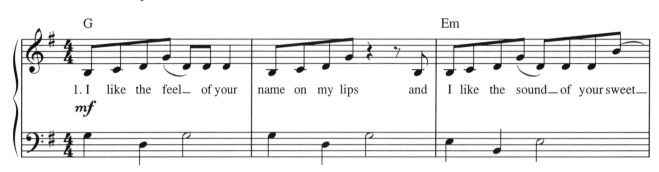

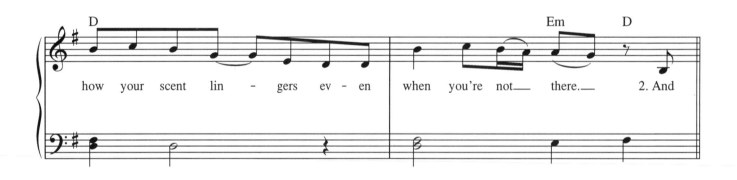

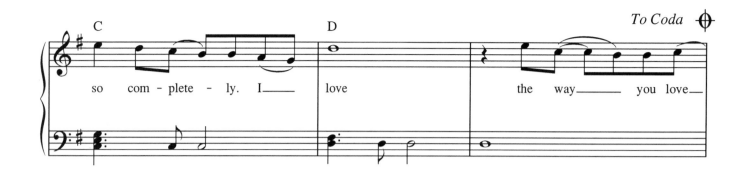

so com - plete - ly. I___ love the way___ you love___

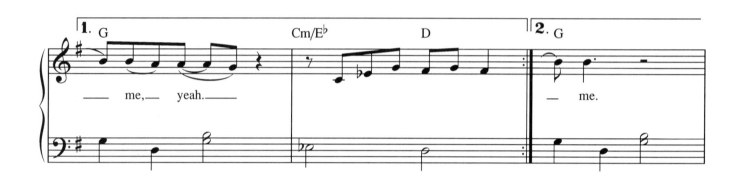

1. ___ me,___ yeah.___ ___ **2.** ___ me.

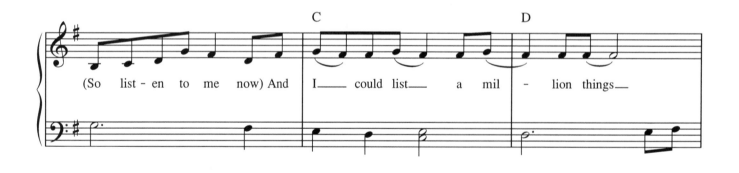

(So list - en to me now) And I___ could list___ a mil - lion things___

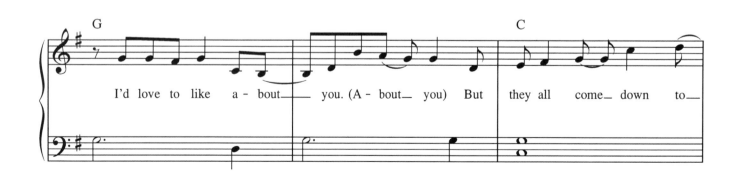

I'd love to like a - bout___ you. (A - bout___ you) But they all come___ down to___

D.S. al Coda

one— rea - son, I could ne - ver live___ with - out___ you. I

CODA

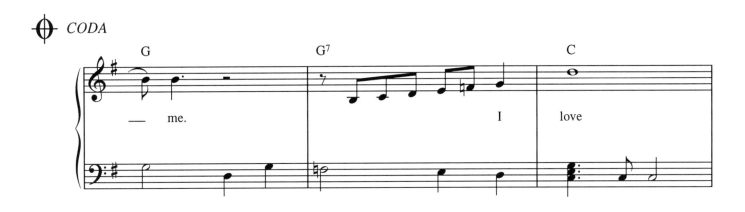

___ me. I love

the way___ that you love___ me.___

Verse 3:

And I like the sound of old R and B
You roll your eyes when I'm slightly off key
And I like the innocent way that you cry
From sappy old movies you've seen thousands of times.

But I love *etc.*

Love Me For A Reason

Words & Music by Johnny Bristol, Wade Brown, Jr. & David Jones

Moderately

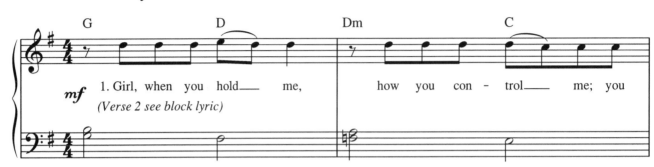

mf 1. Girl, when you hold⸺ me, how you con - trol⸺ me; you
(Verse 2 see block lyric)

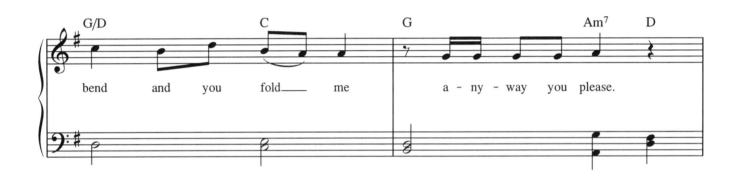

bend and you fold⸺ me a - ny - way you please.

It must be ea - sy for⸺ you, the love - ly things that you⸺ do are

just a pas - time for⸺ you, I could ne - ver be.

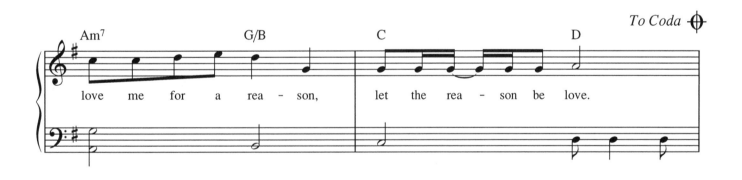

1. let the rea - son be love.

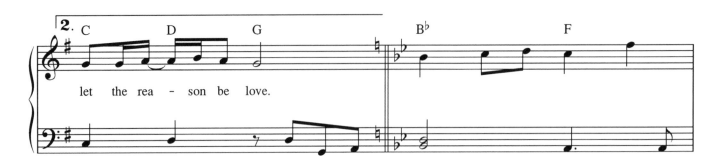

2. let the rea - son be love.

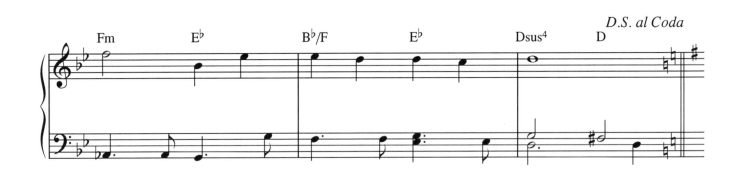

D.S. al Coda

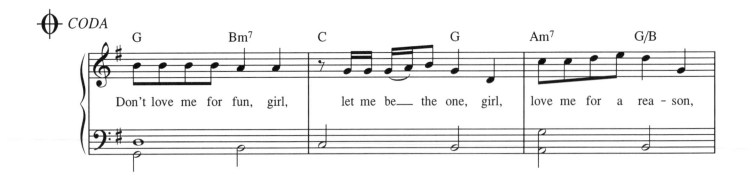

⊕ *CODA*

Don't love me for fun, girl, let me be— the one, girl, love me for a rea - son,

let the rea - son be love. Don't love me for fun, girl, let me be— the one, girl,

love me for a rea - son, let the rea - son be love. Don't love me for fun, girl,

let me be__ the one, girl, love me for a rea - son, let the rea - son be love.

Verse 2:

Kisses and caresses are only minor tests, babe,
Of love needs and stresses between a woman and a man.
So if love everlasting isn't what you're asking,
I'll have to pass, girl; I'm proud to take a stand.
I can't continue guessing, because it's only messing
With my pride and my mind.
So write down this time to time:

To Chorus

D.S.:

I'm just a little old-fashioned,
It takes more than a physical attraction.
My initial reaction is "Honey, give me love;
Not a facsimile of."

To Chorus

Picture Of You

Words & Music by Eliot Kennedy, Ronan Keating, Paul Wilson & Andy Watkins

Moderately

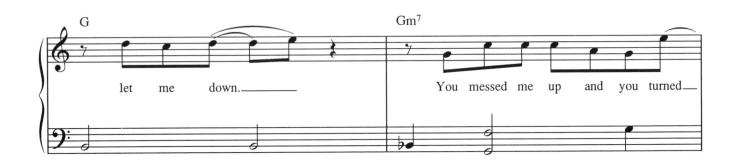

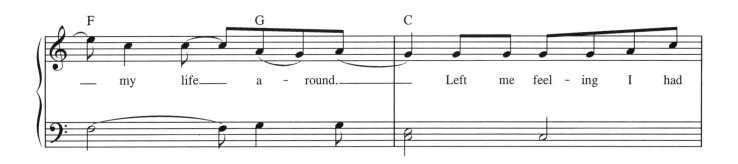

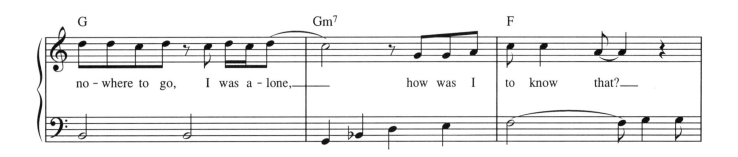

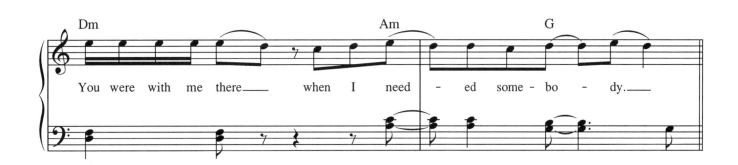

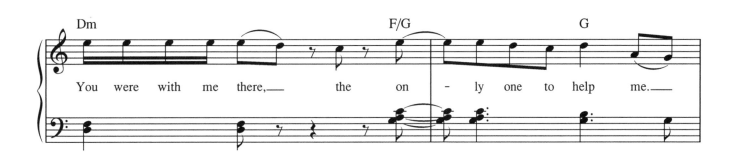

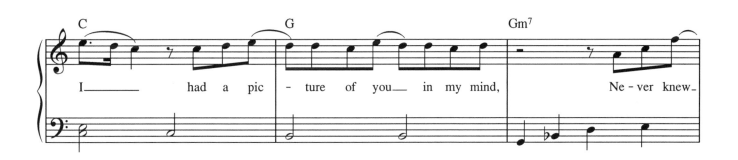

it could be— so wrong,— Why'd it take— me so long— just to find

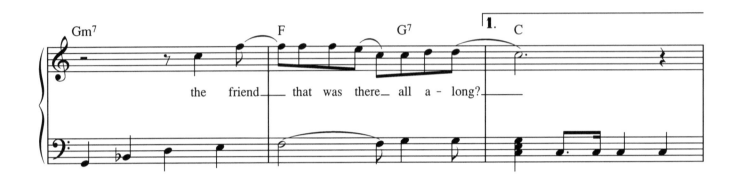

the friend— that was there— all a - long?

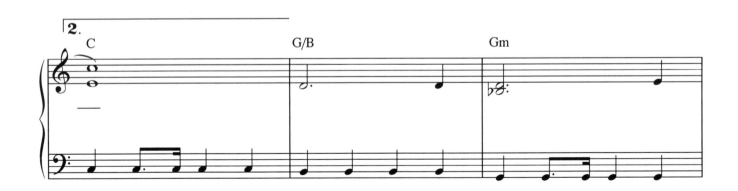

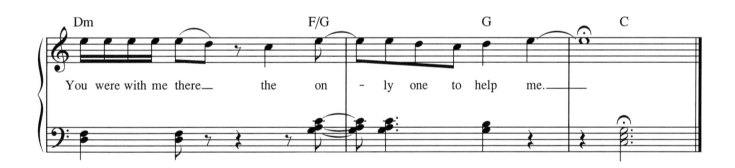

You were with me there___ when I need - ed some - bo - dy.___

You were with me there___ the on - ly one to help me.___

Verse 3:

Did you believe that after all that we've been through
I'd be able to put my trust in you?
Goes to show you can forgive and forget
Looking back I have no regrets, 'cos

You were with me there *etc.*

No Matter What

Music by Andrew Lloyd Webber
Lyrics by Jim Steinman

Moderately

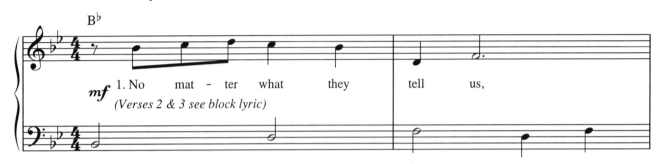

1. No mat - ter what they tell us,
(Verses 2 & 3 see block lyric)

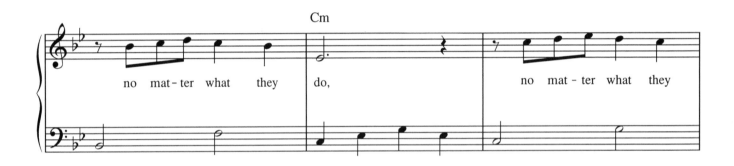

no mat - ter what they do,   no mat - ter what they

teach us,   what we be - lieve is true.

No mat - ter what they call us,   how - ev - er they at -

- tack,   no mat - ter where they take us,

we'll find our own way back.   I can't de - ny___ what

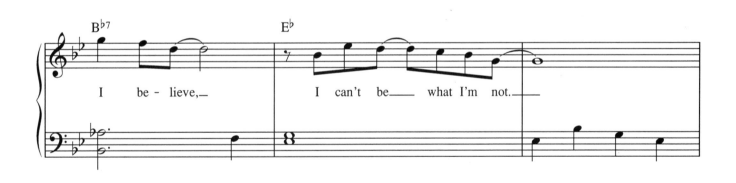

I be - lieve,___ I can't be___ what I'm not.___

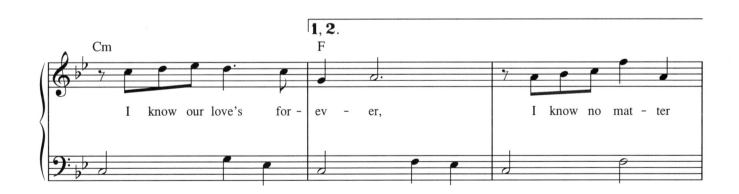

I know our love's for - ev - er,   I know no mat - ter

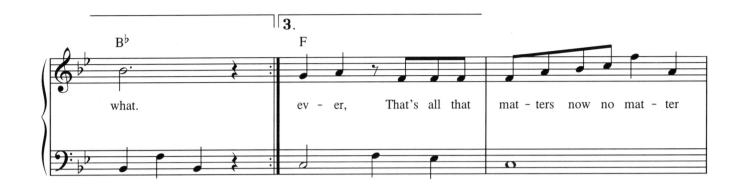

what.   ev - er,   That's all that   mat - ters now no mat - ter

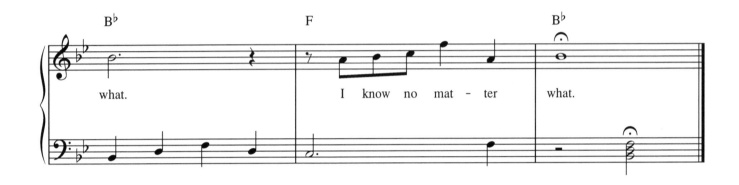

what.   I know no mat - ter   what.

Verse 2:

If only tears were laughter,
If only night was day,
If only prayers were answered
Then we would hear God say.
No matter what they tell us,
No matter what they do,
No matter what they teach you,
What you believe is true.
And I will keep you safe and strong
And sheltered from the storm.
No matter where it's barren
Our dream is being born.

Verse 3:
Instrumental:

No matter if the sun don't shine,
Or if the skies are blue.
No matter what the ending,
My life began with you.
I can't deny what I believe,
I can't be what I'm not.
I know this love's for ever,
That's all that matters now no matter what.

When You Say Nothing At All

Words & Music by Paul Overstreet & Don Schlitz

Moderately

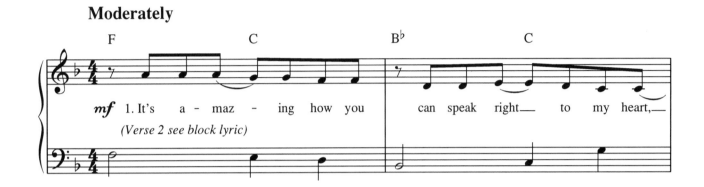

mf 1. It's a - maz - ing how you can speak right___ to my heart,___
(Verse 2 see block lyric)

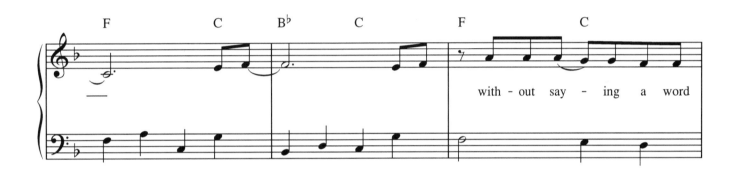

with - out say - ing a word

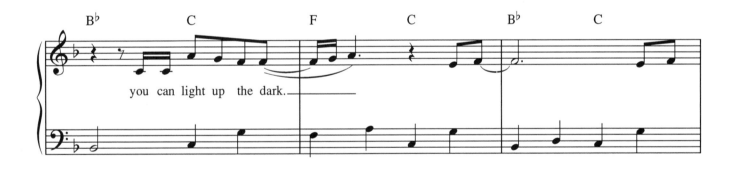

you can light up the dark.___

Try as I may I can ne - ver ex - plain___ what I hear___ when you don't___

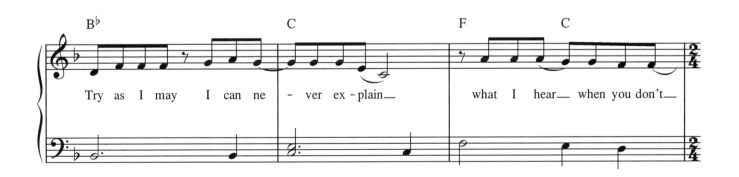

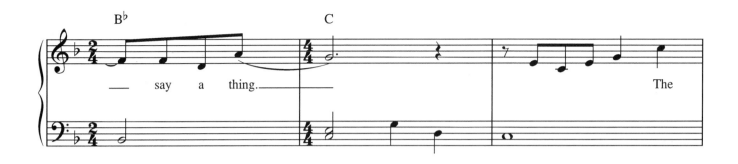

_ say a thing._ The

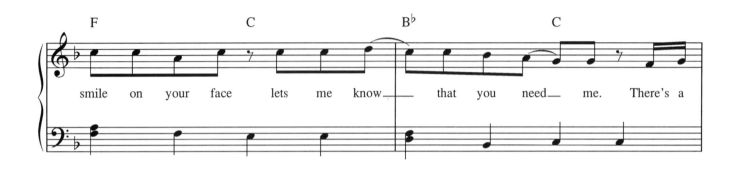

smile on your face lets me know_ that you need_ me. There's a

truth in your eyes say-ing you'll_ ne-ver leave_ me. The touch of your hand says you'll catch_

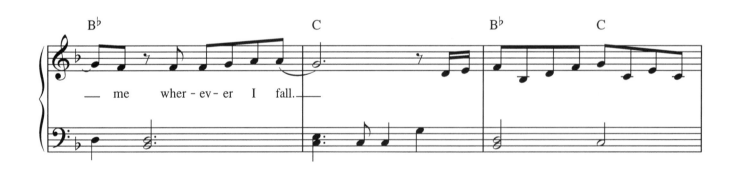

_ me wher-ev-er I fall._

You_ say it best when you say no-thing at all._

me wher - ev - er I fall.

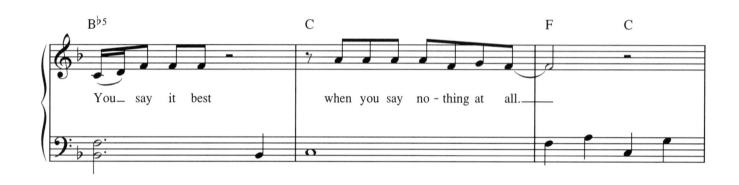

You__ say it best   when you say no - thing at   all.__

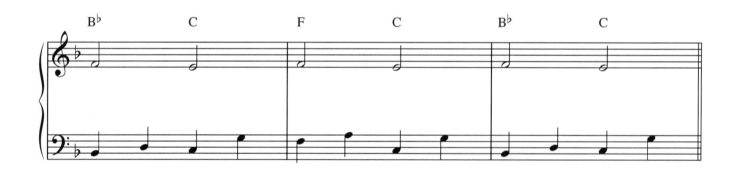

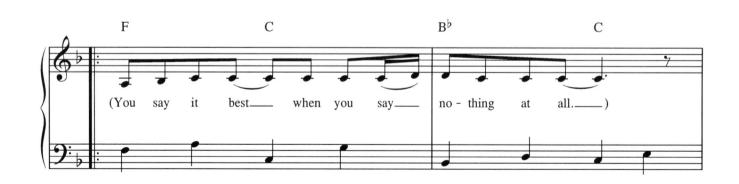

(You   say it best__   when you   say__   no - thing   at   all.__)

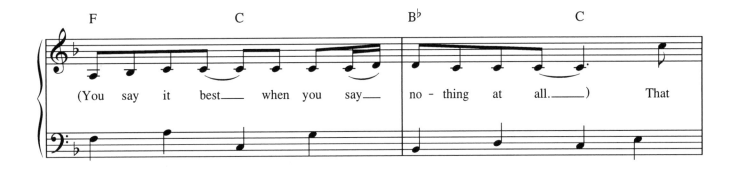

(You say it best__ when you say__ no - thing at all.__) That

smile on your face,__ there's truth in your eyes.__ The

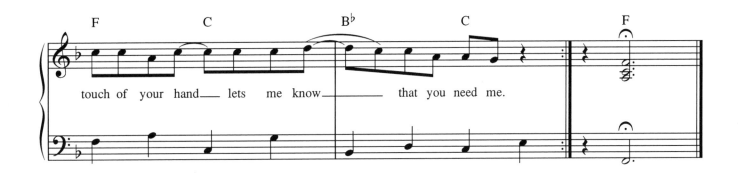

touch of your hand__ lets me know__ that you need me.

Verse 2:

All day long I can hear people talking out loud
But when you hold me you drown out the crowd
Try as they may they can never defy
What's been said between your heart and mine.

The smile on your face *etc.*

You Needed Me

Words & Music by Randy Goodrum

Moderately

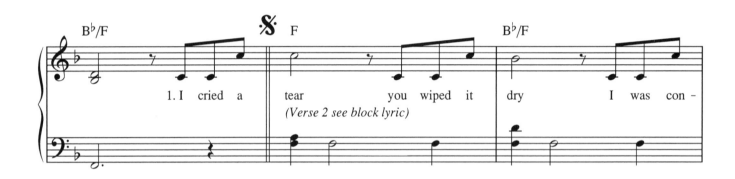

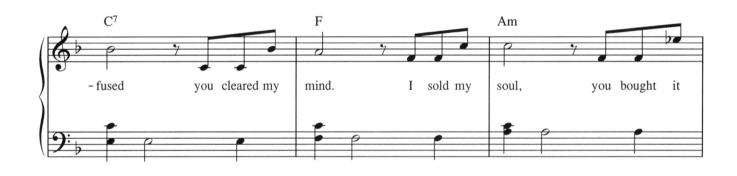

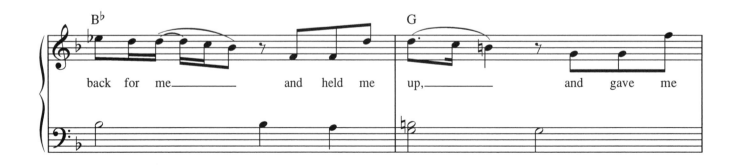

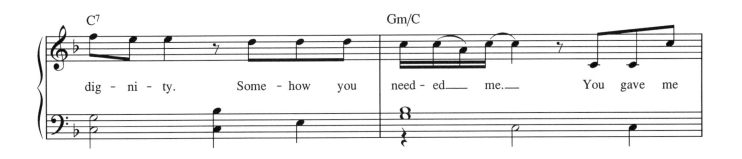

dig – ni – ty.   Some – how you   need – ed_ me._   You gave me

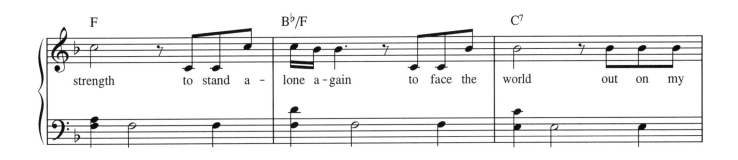

strength   to stand a –   lone a – gain   to face the   world   out on my

own a – gain._   You put me   high   up – on a   pe – de – stal_   so

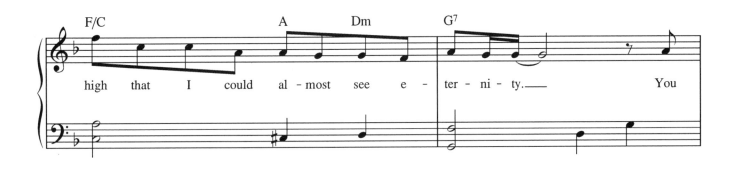

high that I could al – most see   e – ter – ni – ty._   You

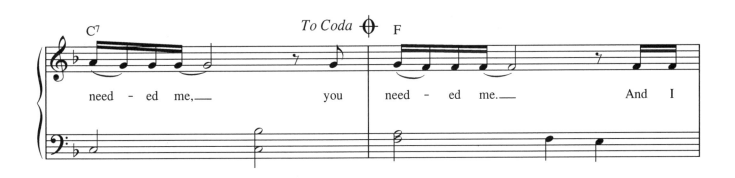

need – ed me,_   you   need – ed me._   And I

can't be-lieve it's you,___ I can't_ be-lieve it's true._____ I

need - ed you,_____ and you were there. And I'll

ne - ver leave why should__ I leave__ I'd be a fool___ 'cos I've

D.S. al Coda

fin-'lly found some-one who real-ly__ cares.__ (You need-ed me) 2. You held my

44

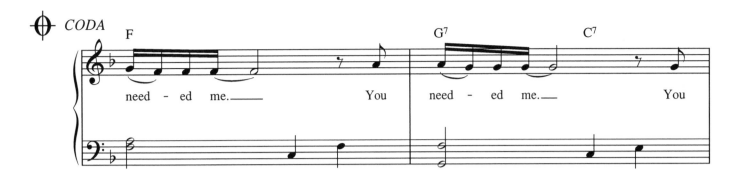

CODA

need - ed me.___ You need - ed me.___ You

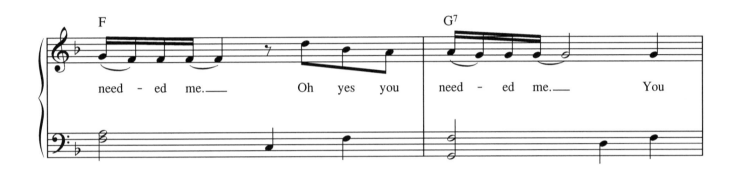

need - ed me.___ Oh yes you need - ed me.___ You

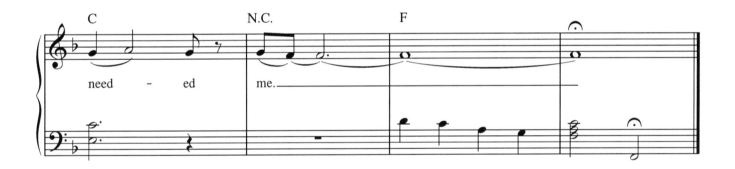

need - ed me.___

Verse 2:

You held my hand
When it was cold
When I was lost
You took me home
You gave me hope
When I was at the end
And turned my lies
Back into truth again
You even called me friend.

You gave me strength
To stand alone again *etc.*

Words

Words & Music by Barry Gibb, Robin Gibb & Maurice Gibb

Moderately slow

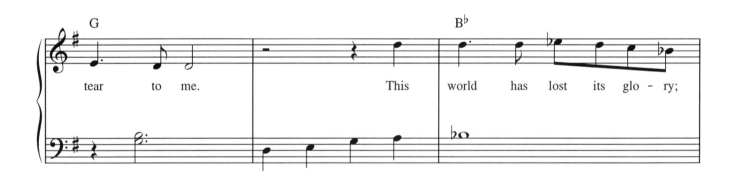

now, there'll be no oth - er time, and I can show you how, my

love.____ Talk in ev - er - last - ing words and ded - i - cate them

all to me. And I will give you all my

life, I'm here if you should call to me. You

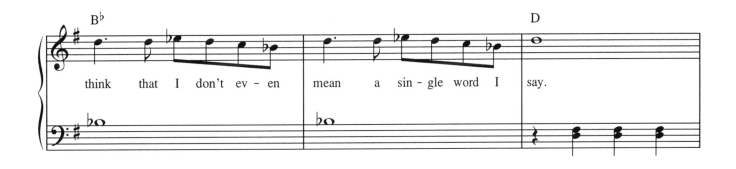

think that I don't ev - en mean a sin - gle word I say.

It's on - ly words, and words are all I have to take your heart a -

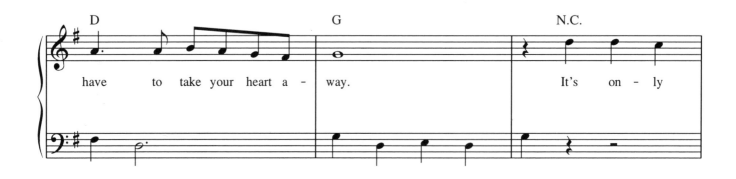

- way. It's on - ly words, and words are all I

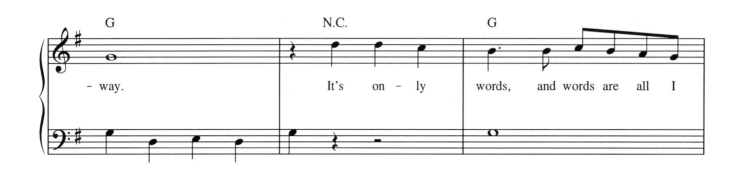

have to take your heart a - way. It's on - ly

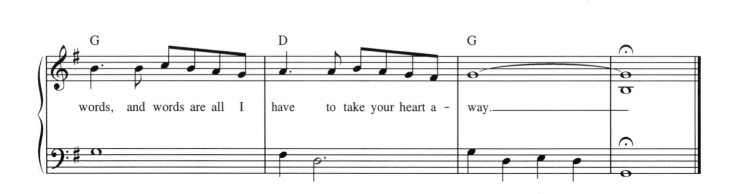

words, and words are all I have to take your heart a - way.____